HOPSCOTCH HISTORIES

Ben's Escape from the Blitz

by Margaret Nash

Illustrated by Mike Spoor

W

FRANKLIN WATTS

LONDON•SYDNEY

About this book

Some of the characters in this book are made up but the story is based on real events in history. World War II began on 1st September 1939. The Blitz (which means 'lightning' in German) started on 7th Sepetmber 1940 when Germany launched daily bomb attacks on Britain. Many children were evacuated to the countryside, away from the risk of bombing. To stop enemy planes loaded with bombs flying too close to London and other cities, the British Army put up barrage balloons. In 1940, there were 1,400 balloons in the skies, but they could fall down during bad storms.

First published in 2009 by
Franklin Watts
338 Euston Road
London
NW1 3BH

Franklin Watts Australia
Level 17/207 Kent Street
Sydney
NSW 2000

Text © Margaret Nash 2009
Illustrations © Mike Spoor 2009

The right of Margaret Nash to be identified as the author
and Mike Spoor as illustrator of this Work has been asserted
in accordance with the Copyright, Designs and Patents Act, 1988.

A CIP catalogue record for this book is available
from the British Library.

ISBN 978 0 7496 8578 2 (hbk)
ISBN 978 0 7496 8584 3 (pbk)

Series Editor: Melanie Palmer
Series Advisor: Dr Barrie Wade
Series Designer: Peter Scoulding

Printed in China

Franklin Watts is a division of
Hachette Children's Books,
an Hachette UK company
www.hachette.co.uk

BANG! BOOM!

Every night, planes were

dropping bombs over London.

"You must go to the countryside where it is safe," Ben's mum said. So she sent Ben to stay on a farm with her friend, Mrs Popple.

5

"Don't worry Ben, it's quiet here. Nothing ever happens," said Mrs Popple as she met Ben at the station.

Ben helped on Mrs Popple's farm.

He collected eggs and fed the pigs.

He collected the coal every night
for Mrs Popple's fire.

Ben wrote a letter to his mum:

" ... Mrs Popple is nice, but life is very quiet. There's another boy called Tony here who left his home too."

10

At school, some of the local boys
teased Ben and Tony.

"Townies! Townies!" they shouted.

"Bet you're afraid of the dark."

"Bet we're not!" said Ben.

"Then prove it. Dare you to come out tonight," they challenged.

Mrs Popple was not happy.

She would not let Ben go out.

"It's too dangerous in the blackout,"

she told him.

Next day at school, the boys came up to Ben and laughed as he and Tony had not shown up.

A week later, there was a terrible storm. It woke up Ben and Tony.

Mrs Popple rushed outside to check on the animals.

Then – CRASH! Something had hit the roof. The hens squawked, the pigs grunted and the dogs barked.

"What if it's a soldier with a gun?" asked Tony, shaking.

"Let's go and see," said Ben.

Tony and Ben peeked outside, but it was all dark. So Ben grabbed a torch and opened the door.

Something huge was hanging down
from the roof. Ben shone his torch
to see what it was.

"Gosh!" said Tony, "What is it?"

"We'd better get help," said Ben.

"Let's find a policeman. Hurry!"

They ran down a dark lane.

They splashed through puddles.

They almost bumped into a horse.

Then they saw a policeman.

"Help!" they cried.

"What are you both up to?"
the policeman said. "You should
be in bed."

"Quick! There's something on our roof – it might explode!" said Toby. "Calm down lad, nothing happens around here," the policeman said.

The policeman was surprised
when he got to the house.
"A barrage balloon!" he cried.
"This is a job for the army."

"Well done lads!" a soldier said.
We put these balloons in the sky to
stop enemy planes flying too low
and dropping bombs on our towns."

Next day at school, everyone knew about the balloon. They cheered Ben and Tony. And no one said they were afraid of the dark again.

Puzzle 1

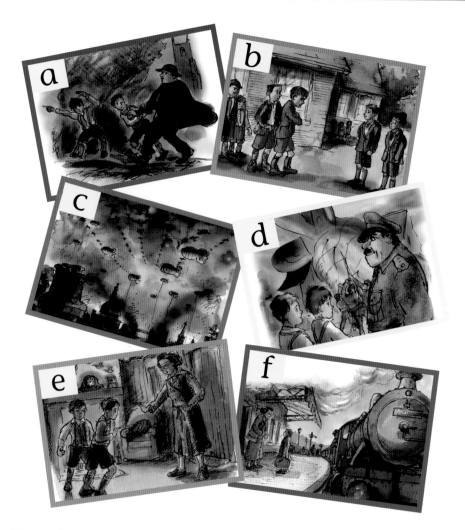

Put these pictures in the correct order.

Which event do you think is most important?

Now try writing the story in your own words!

Puzzle 2

Word Bank

Army
Blackout
Bomb
City
Countryside
Train

What do these pictures tell you about

World War II and the way of life at the time?

How are things different today?

You can use the word bank to help you.

Answers

Puzzle 1

The correct order is: 1c, 2f, 3b, 4e, 5a, 6d.

Puzzle 2

Life in Britain was very different in World War II.

Think about rationing, blackouts, evacuees and air raids.

To find out more, try this book:

Children and World War II, (History Snapshots), Sarah Ridley, Franklin Watts, 2007.

Look out for more Hopscotch Histories:

Henry VIII Has to Choose
ISBN 978 0 7496 8573 7*
ISBN 978 0 7496 8579 9

The King and the Great Fire
ISBN 978 0 7496 8575 1*
ISBN 978 0 7496 8581 2

Florence and the Drummer Boy
ISBN 978 0 7496 8574 4*
ISBN 978 0 7496 8580 5

Ben's Escape from the Blitz
ISBN 978 0 7496 8578 2*
ISBN 978 0 7496 8584 3

The Song of Boudica
ISBN 978 0 7496 8576 8*
ISBN 978 0 7496 8582 9

Eric Bloodaxe, the Viking King
ISBN 978 0 7496 8577 5*
ISBN 978 0 7496 8583 6

Toby and the Great Fire of London
ISBN 978 0 7496 7410 6

Hoorah for Mary Seacole
ISBN 978 0 7496 7413 7

Remember Remember the 5th of November
ISBN 978 0 7496 7414 4

Pocahontas the Peacemaker
ISBN 978 0 7496 7080 1*
ISBN 978 0 7496 7411 3

Grandma's Seaside Bloomers
ISBN 978 0 7496 7412 0

Tutankhamun and the Golden Chariot
ISBN 978 0 7496 7084 9*
ISBN 978 0 7496 7415 1

For more Hopscotch books go to: www.franklinwatts.co.uk

*hardback